The Best Party Dresses

CONTENTS

trends to watch

Fabulous

Hot List!

Need Pink S Nail

Barbie ™

Hey there!

I'm so glad you dropped by! Welcome to my brand new 2013 Annual. Prepare to be dazzled each time you turn a page, because it's simply stuffed with brilliant things to do. There are make-its, recipes, quizzes, games and all sorts of amazing activities inside. And, whether you love reading to yourself or curling up on the sofa and being read to, you're in for a special treat with my two terrific new stories. So come on, what are you waiting for? Step in to my world!

Barbie xxx

Pedigree®

Published 2012.
Pedigree Books Limited, Beech Hill House,
Walnut Gardens, Exeter, Devon EX4 4DH
www.pedigreebooks.com
books@pedigreegroup.co.uk

£7.99

Backstage With Barbie

Not only will they totally rock, it's a chance for me to hang out with all my friends and my sisters too. I love music so much and I recently bumped into the L.A. Ladeez at one of my film premieres so I've managed to score backstage passes for everyone — including you! Check out my pass and then add your own deets into the blank pass opposite.

This weekend I'm off to watch a pop concert with the special people in my life. You can catch up with all my gang over the next few pages. I'm sure you and I have loads in common. Acting and singing are my passions but I also love animals and spending time with my friends and family. That's why I'm so excited about seeing the L.A. Ladeez playing live.

L.a. ladeez
WORLD TOUR 2013
Backstage Pass

NAME: Barbie

HEIGHT: 170 cm

EYE COLOUR: Sky blue

HAIR: Golden Blonde, Waist length

FAVE COLOUR: Pink

L.a. ladeez
WORLD TOUR 2013
Backstage Pass

NAME: ....

HEIGHT: ....

EYE COLOUR: ....

HAIR: ....

FAVE COLOUR: ....

Check out my pass and then add your own deets into the blank pass.

Place or draw a picture of yourself!

Backstage With

Skipper

There's nothing more important than family, right?

And I'm super close to my three amazing sisters. I love to hang out with them at the beach or have sister sleepovers. Let me introduce you!

Skipper is so smart and creative. She's really into technology and has her own cool blog

L.a. ladees
WORLD TOUR 2013
Backstage Pass

NAME: Skipper

HEIGHT: 155 cm

EYE COLOUR: Lavender

HAIR: Brunette with coloured streaks

Stacie

Stacie is as energetic and athletic as my friend Summer and is on every school sports team.

We share a love of animals — she has such a cute guinea pig!

L.a. ladeez WORLD TOUR 2013 Backstage Pass

NAME: Stacie

HEIGHT: 137 cm

EYE COLOUR: Blue

HAIR: Blonde, Shoulder-length

Chelsea

L.a. ladeez WORLD TOUR 2 Backstage Pass

NAME: Chelsea

HEIGHT: 107 cm

EYE COLOUR: Blue

HAIR: Blonde, Shoulder-length

And then there's Chelsea! She's so adorable and fun and is a born performer just like me. The great thing about the concert is that it's taking place in the afternoon, which means I can bring all my sisters along!

Backstage With

Teresa

Let me introduce you to my two BFFs.

Teresa and I have been friends, like, forever! Since we were four actually. She's so sweet and down-to-earth and we have so much in common. She's a brilliant actress and she loves animals even more than I do — if that's even possible.

She's got a real way with them and is always bringing home strays. We love to go horse-riding together. Oh, and did I mention, she bakes the best cupcakes in the world!

L.A. Jadees WORLD TOUR 2013 **Backstage** Pass

NAME: Teresa

HEIGHT: 173 cm

EYE COLOUR: Hazel

HAIR: Brown, Long

Nikki

Now to Nikki! What can I say, the girl's got style. She's always on top of the latest trends and knows all the coolest places in town. We met in high school when we were both up for the same movie role.

She's an actress too, but she's also an incredible dancer and a great photographer!

L.a. ladees WORLD TOUR 2013
Backstage Pass

NAME: Nikki

HEIGHT: 173 cm

EYE COLOUR: Brown

HAIR: Dark brown, Long

Backstage With

Raquelle

What can I tell you about my friend Raquelle. You might already have seen her around town or on TV. She's pretty hard to miss because, as well as being a huge star, she's absolutely stunning!

Raquelle can be a bit of a diva and sometimes she can be tricky to get along with, but she can also be charming and she's Ryan's sister, so she's always going to be part of the crowd.

L.a. ladeez WORLD TOUR 2013
Backstage Pass

NAME: Raquelle

HEIGHT: 178 cm

EYE COLOUR: Blue

HAIR: Black, Waist length

Summer

Summer is my go-to gal if I want to do something energetic like take a hike in the Hollywood hills or have a run on the beautiful sandy beach in Malibu. Summer's a world-class tennis player — we met when I needed coaching for a movie-role as a tennis champion.

She's often away competing, but we call each other all the time and catch up whenever she's home. I just love hanging with Summer. Here name says it all. She's always sunny, just like a summer's day.

L.a. ladeez WORLD TOUR 2013 **Backstage** Pass

NAME: Summer

HEIGHT: 170 cm

EYE COLOUR: Green

HAIR: Reddish brown, Long

Backstage With

The Boys

Meet my guys. I love hanging with these three guys. They're all so funny and cool.

Ken is especially fun to be around plus he's really loyal and reliable, if he says he's going to meet you for asmoothie and a chat, then he's there. He's also really sporty. I love to go to the beach and watch him surf!

L.a. ladeez WORLD TOUR 2013 Backstage Pass

NAME: Ken

HEIGHT: 188 cm

EYE COLOUR: Blue

HAIR: Blonde

And of course there's Ryan. He shares my love of music and he's an amazing guitarist and songwriter. I'm so lucky to have such great friends that are talented and share my interests.

L.a. ladeez
WORLD TOUR 2013
Backstage Pass

NAME: Ryan

HEIGHT: 190 cm

EYE COLOUR: Brown

HAIR: Dark Brown

L.a. ladeez
WORLD TOUR 2013
Backstage Pass

NAME: Steven

HEIGHT: 183 cm

EYE COLOUR: Honey Brown

HAIR: Dark Brown

I've known Steven since we were little. He and Ken are great friends so we often hang out together and he wants to be a Hollywood agent one day, so he loves listen to stories about the movies I've worked on.

special friendship

Fab

scrapbook

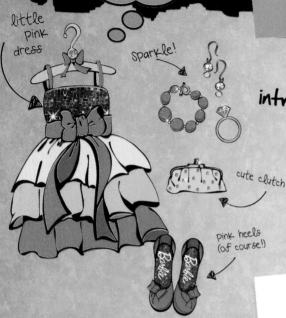

little pink dress

sparkle!

cute clutch

pink heels (of course!)

Now you've learnt more about me and have been introduced to all my friends, it's time for you to let me sneak a peek at your life.

Add your pics here..

Scrapbooking is a great way to bring together a collection of special mementoes around a theme, so use these pages to create a scrapbook about you and your BFFs.

Add your pics here..

100% Fabulous

You could include anything from party invites and concert tickets which remind you of fun times spent together, to cool snapshots of your pals, drawings you've done or notes you've written to each other.

Add your pics here...

omg

love Barbie

Use glue or tape to stick them on the pages, overlapping to fit as many items in as possible. That's the fun of scrapbooking... it's not about being neat, it's about creating fun, colourful and lasting memories.

Glam Girl

Hot List!

Cute Shoes

trends to watch

Need More PINK SPARKLY Nail POLish

Fab

Barbie

When two worlds collide, the results can be magical...

THE Popstar

CAST:

PRINCESS TORI

KEIRA

CRIDER

RUPERT

DUCHESS AMELIA

PRINCE LIAM

19

Princess Victoria sighed as she looked at the line of dignitaries stretching through the royal reception hall. Being Princess of the kingdom of Meribella and meeting handsome princes from neighbouring kingdoms was all very nice, but tonight she wanted to be somewhere else – the royal amphitheatre, watching her favourite popstar, Keira perform.

There was no escaping her duty tonight however, especially under the watchful eyes of her father The King and her aunt, The Duchess Amelia. So, Tori gracefully accepted her guests and welcomed each of them in turn.

Even dutiful princesses need to have fun however and when, later that evening, The King and Duchess Amelia gathered the guests together for the unveiling of the latest royal portrait, they were shocked to discover a painting of a donkey. The King suppressed a smile, but Duchess Amelia was furious at the pranksters - Tori and her sisters Meredith and Trevi, who were in fits of laughter on the balcony.

"Princess Victoria Bethany Evangeline Renée!" she stormed. "It's time you started acting like a Princess of the Realm, not some silly schoolgirl!"

And the angry Duchess sent Tori to her room for the rest of the evening to work on her Commemoration speech.

"I wish I had her life, I'd be another me!" sighed Tori, gazing wistfully at a poster of Keira the popstar on her wall and thinking that Keira's life must be much more exciting.

Keira's life was exciting, but it was also exhausting. Her performance that night had gone brilliantly. The audience had adored her new song 'Here I Am'. But even off stage, Keira couldn't relax. She argued with her slippery manager Crider about telling the record company they could have preview of the new songs she was writing, when they weren't yet ready.

Then she rushed through her schedule with assistant Nora, telling her to accept an invitation to the castle for tea the next day. Shutting everyone out of her dressing room, Keira sank down on a couch and cuddled her puppy, Riff.

"I don't get it. Writing songs used to be fun. Don't get me wrong, Riff. I mean, I'm a star; I'm livin' the dream, right?? It's just I sometimes wonder what it'd be like to Just. Let. Go."

"Princess Victoria!" she sighed to Riff, spotting an enormous poster of the Royal Family displayed by the side of the stage. "Now there's a sweet gig. Lives in a castle, everything done for her. She's probably never worked a day in her life…"

So while Princess Tori, in her palatial bedroom, was busy gazing at her posters of Keira and dreaming of being a popstar, Keira, backstage at the amphitheatre, was trying her best to imagine life as a princess – a princess like Tori.

The next afternoon the princess and the popstar met at the palace.
"A real, live princess. Awesome!" Keira exclaimed.
"You're Keira!" Tori smiled, taking her idol's hand. "I'm absolutely your biggest fan."

The excited pair had no idea that two people close to them were scheming. Duchess Amelia, intent on seeing Tori do her duty had lined up a possible suitor – Prince Liam - to meet her niece, while Keira's manager Crider had the Duchess herself in his sights. Crider, a former popstar was resentful that his career had stalled while Keira's sky-rocketed.

"If only I had the means to restart my career…" he thought as he shook Duchess Amelia's hand. "All I need is one lucky break… or a rich widow."

While Crider tried to win Duchess Amelia over, Tori showed Keira the palace. Keira was amazed by all Tori's fan posters and memorabilia and stunned to hear her sing 'Here I Am'.

"When I was little, I always dreamed of being a princess, wearing a ballgown and tiara," Keira admitted. So Tori put her tiara on Keira's head.

"Formal Gown Number 9" said Keira, into her microphone and in a flash she was magically dressed in the same gown as Tori. "So that's how you change so quickly", laughed Tori, "I have something like that!" And with a wave of her magic hairbrush her hair changed to match Keira's purple locks.

Then, pointing their magical objects at each other each girl whispered some words until... Whoosh! With a shower of sparkles they transformed into each other.

Tori and Keira simply couldn't believe that they'd switched identities. Tori now looked like a cool popstar with purple hair, while Keira was a stunning blonde in a pink ballgown. The new BFFs giggled as they continued their tour of the castle, fooling everyone from the dashing and gallant Prince Liam to Tori's sister and the King himself.

Finally Tori showed Keira a secret garden where an amazing diamond-producing gardenia plant was protected by magical garden fairies.

"It blooms just once every five years," Tori told Keira. "Its diamonds help pay for schools and stuff."

As the girls watched, two tiny diamonds appeared at the base of the plant. The fairies placed the diamonds into the necklaces the girls were already wearing.

"These will be our Friendship Necklaces." Tori beamed.

But oh dear! Suddenly Duchess Amelia appeared.

"Are you mad, bringing an outsider in here?" she yelled at the girl she thought was her niece, but was in fact Keira.

Tori pulled Keira back into the castle quickly and the Duchess was busy being angry that no-one saw Crider in the doorway. He'd seen the diamond plant and was rubbing his hands in wicked glee...

To be continued...

27

POP-TASTIC WORDSEARCH

It's not easy being a popstar. As Princess Tori discovered in the story, there are lots of things to think about when putting on a performance. All the words in the list below are hidden within the grid. Can you find them all?

Find these words:

1. AUTOGRAPH
2. BACKING SINGERS
3. BASS
4. CHOREOGRAPHY
5. COSTUMES
6. CROWD
7. DANCERS
8. DRUMS
9. ENCORE
10. GUITAR
11. KEYBOARD
12. MICROPHONE
13. SONGS
14. STAGE

S	A	U	T	O	G	R	A	P	H	S	S
R	B	Y	E	K	E	Y	B	O	A	R	D
E	C	O	A	E	C	H	L	W	S	E	E
G	E	A	E	Y	R	P	S	D	R	S	R
N	S	R	E	C	N	A	D	T	B	O	O
I	E	A	A	B	M	R	O	N	A	N	C
S	M	I	T	O	I	G	W	U	R	G	N
G	U	T	A	A	C	O	A	I	A	S	E
N	T	A	S	R	G	E	D	O	T	U	A
I	S	O	H	D	U	R	O	R	I	O	C
K	O	B	L	D	W	O	R	C	U	O	O
C	C	L	O	R	C	H	O	R	G	M	Y
A	A	B	A	S	S	C	O	N	G	P	S
B	T	E	N	O	H	P	O	R	C	I	M

There are also two hidden words which are not on the list and which relate to being a princess. Can you find them?

1. T _ _ _ _
2. B _ _ _ _ _ _

STORY SPOT
THE DIFFERENCE

Tori and Keira made the perfect musical duo, didn't they?

Here they are again, practicing a duet. There are six differences between picture A and picture B. Can you find and ring them. Colour in a guitar each time you spot one.

BUSY BARBIE

My life is just so crazy at the moment; it's hard to keep track of what I'm doing. Check out my busy schedule below, and copy everything I need to do onto the colourful reminder notes stuck all over my fridge door.

My Schedule

THINGS TO DO

Call Ken this evening
Bake cupcakes for Teresa's party
Pack for NYC
Run lines with Kelly

What's your life like this week?
Why not add your own appointments onto the reminder notes.

SHOPPING LIST
Sequin needs a new colla[r]
Pink sparkly nail polish
I'm all out of glitter!

My Schedule

SHOPPING LIST

APPOINTMENTS

Fridge

THINGS TO DO

Fabulous

THINGS TO REMEMBER

trends to watch

Barbie

31

CCT
Clever Closet Tips

When you love clothes and shoes as much as I do, you need to be savvy when it comes to your closet. If I didn't have systems in place to keep my clothes tidy and accessible, I'd never be ready in time to make a red carpet event or meet my friends. Now we're BFFs, I'm more than happy to pass on my top tips for a cool closet.

Get Organized
Splitting your wardrobe into segments makes it easier to find the exact piece you want to wear. You can section by...
- Colour - putting items of a particular shade together
- Garment type - hanging tops together, then jeans, then dresses...
- Season – creating areas for spring and summer wear and autumn and winter styles.

Picture This
To protect your shoes and keep them tidy why not photograph each pair and then stick the photo to the outside of the shoe box they're stored in. That way you can locate those beaded flip-flops without having to open every shoebox in the process.

signature & classic!

add a little sparkle

Barbie

new boots make the outfit!

love them all!

...te shoes + the perfect bag = Amazing!

Makes Good Scents
You want your clothes to smell as good as they look. So, line drawers with pretty wrapping paper place scented soaps or bags of pot pourri in you're the corners to make sure everything smells gorgeous.

Pret-a-Porter
Fashionistas like you will know this means 'ready to wear'! So to ensure yours are just that, make sure that you never put anything back in the wardrobe unless it's in perfect, wearable condition. That means carrying out little repairs, replacing buttons etc., the moment they happen.

Sorted
Make sure the things you wear most often are easily accessible to you and those, which you might only need on occasion, are stored higher up or at the back of the wardrobe.

Barbie

Reality Check
Closet space is so precious; you need to be honest with yourself about the items that fill it. Take a look at each piece and if you haven't worn it for a while ask yourself if you could update it by adding a personal twist like beads, fringing or a colourful stencil. If not and you haven't worn it for at least a year, recycle it by giving it to a friend or local charity shop. Remember! One girl's trash is another girl's treasure.

PERFECT PLATES

Malibu

Shopping

California is such a huge State and I love to discover new unspoilt corners in my cute, convertible. Whether I'm off on a shopping trip, driving to a café to meet friends or simply cruising the Malibu coastline, I don't know where I'd be without my car. You've seen my personalized number plates, but have you thought about how yours might look?

Use your favourite pens to create an eye-popping and unique design on the plate bbelow.

CALIFORNIA
Barbie

California

CALIFORNIA
IM A DOLL
The Golden State

CALIFORNIA
FAB ₯ LIFE

CALIFORNIA
GLAM GIRL

Tori and Keira ran through the castle back to Tori's room as fast as their legs would carry them. Keira suggested they switch back immediately but Tori was sorry the swap had to end.

"We could change places in the morning, and spend the whole day being each other!" she suggested eagerly. "It'd be magical…"

So the next morning, unaware that her manager Crider was now plotting to steal the diamond plant, Keira came to the castle again and the girls switched identities.

Then Tori headed to the amphitheatre to rehearse with Keira's dancers while Keira went for a drive in the horse-drawn royal carriage. What fun!

The girls had a fabulous time living each other's lives for the day. Keira couldn't get enough of being waited on by servants, while Tori enjoyed the freedom of a simple walk in the city. As she strolled the streets, some of Keira's fans came up to her to ask for Keira's autograph.

"I really, really, wanted to go see your concert!" one girl said sadly.

"Well there's one more show tomorrow night... maybe you can still see her... I mean... me!" replied Tori, remembering the girls thought she was their idol, Keira.

But the girls then told her they couldn't afford things like concert tickets because the people of Meribella were struggling after a big drought. Tori felt ashamed to be so out of touch with her subjects.

That evening Tori and Keira called each other. Keira told Tori about an embarrassing un-princess-like sneezing fit she'd had in front of important guests and Tori told Keira how she'd learnt that the people in her kingdom were suffering. Keira offered to make her last concert a free one and the pair agreed to meet at the amphitheatre that evening so that Keira could perform and Tori could be ready to finally give her speech the following day.

But then, disaster struck. Duchess Amelia came up to Tori's room to find 'her niece' playing the guitar and writing a new song instead of working on the speech. She was so angry she locked Keira in. Keira was due to go on stage at the amphitheatre in less than an hour and she was a prisoner.

"I'm not the Princess! I'm Keira!" Keira yelled through the locked door.

But the Duchess just wouldn't believe her. In desperation Keira tried Tori's phone over and over again, but Tori didn't reply. Tori had left her phone on stage and was now surrounded by stylists doing her hair and make-up, ready for the show. Poor Tori was frantic. Why hadn't Keira turned up so they could change places again? She couldn't perform to thousands of people! Terrified, she found herself pushed onto the stage and into the spotlight…

Meanwhile, back at the palace, Keira peered frantically out of the window. The whole royal family would be at the concert now, could she get a guard's attention? She saw a limo drive up. Crider and a no-good roadie called Rupert stepped out. Keira tried to get her manager's attention but he didn't look up and she couldn't hear him tell the captain of the guards that The Duchess had sent him back to fetch her spectacles.

Crider and Rupert rushed into the palace and straight for the garden where they used hairspray to stick the angry fairies wings together and wrenched the gardenia plant out of its flowerbed by the roots. All around the kingdom, everything natural began to fade and wither. But Crider didn't care. Now he could use the diamonds to resurrect his career.

Up in Tori's room, Tori's clever puppy Vanessa showed Keira a secret passageway behind a painting. Keira ran outside and caught Tori's voice on the night air singing a softer version of 'Here I Am'.

Tori was bravely performing as Keira and the crowd were delighted. But, as she took her bows, she noticed all the surrounding trees fading in colour.

'The Gardenia!' she cried running off stage. She jumped into the King's carriage back to the castle and arrived just in time to find Keira, trying to stop Crider and Rupert who were escaping in another carriage.

"Gotta fly!" Crider called as he rode down the cliff. But he hadn't counted on the courageous girls who zip wired down strings of lights and ambushed the carriage further down the road. It was all over for Crider.

Grabbing the diamond plant, the girls used their magical objects to change back to their real selves for the last time and raced back to the secret garden.

They did their best to replant the gardenia while the fairies – who'd managed to unstick their wings – hovered worriedly over them. But it was no use. "It's dead!" exclaimed Tori.

"Can't you plant another one?" Keira suggested.

"Where do you get seeds for a magical plant?" shrugged Tori, but then she paused. "Unless its diamonds could be its seeds…?"

Quick as a flash she took the diamond from her friendship necklace and Keira did the same. They planted them side-by-side. When the fairies gently watered them they finally began to sprout. Outside the kingdom's plants and trees returned to life.

40

"The concert!" The girls cried. They'd been so busy celebrating they'd forgotten the crowd were still waiting for Keira's return. The friends hurried back to the amphitheatre and Keira jumped straight on stage with her guitar. The audience, including the King, Duchess and Prince Liam couldn't believe it when she dedicated the song to her new best friend Princess Tori and they were even more shocked when Tori ran out on stage to duet with Keira. The girls exchanged smiles; they now appreciated their own lives.

Keira had learnt to have fun making music and Tori to remember her subjects and take her role seriously. The next day she'd give her speech and vow to make Meribella a better place to live, but now it was time for The Princess and the Popstar to ROCK OUT!!!

PRINCESS OR POPSTAR

Can you kick it like Keira or are you totally Tori? Take this fun personality test to find out if you're more 'princess with poise' or 'playful popstar'.

It's the school play tonight do you...

a. miss your break to do one last rehearsal?

b. teach all your classmates how to curtsey beautifully for the curtain call?

Your bedroom is painted...

a. in vibrant purple with tons of posters on the wall.

b. in shades of pink with lots of scatter cushions on the bed.

Your favourite way to spend a Saturday afternoon with friends is...

a. going to a dance class or singing along to CDs in your bedroom.

b. in the hair salon, getting your hair done and reading your favourite magazines.

You go to the cupboard for a snack and choose...

a. a big bag of crisps.

b. a cupcake with swirly icing.

The person you most love hanging out with beside your BFF is...

a. your brother or sister.

b. your mum – she's just fab.

If you could make one wish it would be...

a. for world peace.

b. to stop all cruelty to animals.

Mostly a's.
Your bubbly, vibrant personality means you're never far from the spotlight, but you work as hard as you play. You are a popstar in the making!

Mostly b's
You have the grace and kindheartedness of a true princess. Plus you love to be pampered – and why not!

Barbie's lined up a gig for her band later this month.
Can you pick her out an outfit to wear on stage?
Circle the one you like best.

43

Stage It!

Staging a show, a play or a concert is great fun. It's a wonderful way to bring people together and to showcase talent among your friends. I know a thing or too about being in the spotlight and giving a performance to remember so I've put together this handy guide so you and your friends will give a performance to remember. So come on, what are you waiting for? It's Showtime!

Solo Star or Chorus Girl

The first thing you need to decide is whether you want to go it alone or perform among friends. You might like to sing, play or dance a solo. But if you'd rather share the spotlight you could do a duet, create a choir or perform an ensemble piece.
So whether you're born to perform or just want to have fun with your chums, there's always a spot for you.

Practice Makes Perfect

You'll never succeed if you don't put the work in first, so whether you're doing a dance display, a music recital or a rock concert, practice is key. Get together as many times as possible before the big day and, on the day of the concert, do a full dress rehearsal to make sure everyone knows exactly what they are doing.

Play to your Strengths

Once you've got your friends together, talk about the things you enjoy doing and are good at. Some of you might have tuneful voices, some might play instruments. You may have a drama queen among you who will be great in a dramatic role. There are also lots of other elements involved in putting on a show. Is there a strong character among you, who could act as director or stage manager? Is one of you a fashionista with an eye for style who could create costumes or style a group?

Get a Gig

Now, where will you perform your show or concert? How about your sitting room? What about the garden? Could you perform at your youth club or at Brownies? Have you asked if you could treat your teachers and school pals to a gig at lunchtime in your school hall? You could do an open-air concert at your local park and invite friends and family. There are lots of free venues around so make sure you explore every possibility. But make sure you get permission from grown-ups first.

Lights, costumes, action

Don't neglect all the many things that make a show, a show. Have you thought about hair and make-up? Can you create a mood with clever lighting? Have you arranged snacks for the audience in the interval, or at the end of the show?

Sparkle and Shine

Even the most experienced performers get nervous before they go on stage. So if you're feeling floored by nerves try these things:

1. **Pre-show Ritual.** Your pals are probably feeling as nervous as you, so get together for a group hug. You could also try repeating a positive phrase out loud three or four times, such as "We're going to be great!"

2. **Just Breathe.** When you're nervous your heart beats faster and your breathing becomes shallow and rapid. Take at least three calm, deep breaths before you step out on stage.

3. **Smile.** Your audience is looking forward to seeing you, so the least you can do is look happy to be there. Sticking on a smile will help put you at ease, and, if you focus on getting the first few lines right the rest of the performance will be a breeze.

4. **The show must go on.** If you make a mistake, keep on going. Chances are no one noticed anyway and even if they did, they'll soon forget about it once you hit those high notes or pull off that dazzling dance move.

A magical mermaid and a surfing superstar! Life is about to get complicated for Merliah Summers...

46

Merliah Summers jumped up and down in delight on the sand. She had just won the Laguna Beach Surfing Tournament, which meant she had qualified for the Australian Invitationals. She exchanged excited hugs with her human grandfather, Break, but there was one person in particular she couldn't wait to tell. Her mother, Calissa, Queen of the Merfolk and that meant a trip to Oceana.

"I wish to be a mermaid!" Merliah said, putting on the magic necklace Calissa had given her to help her switch form. In a flash her legs were gone, replaced by a shimmering pink tail.

"Race you to Oceana!" Merliah cried, spotting her best undersea buddy, Snouts the seal bobbing in the water beside her. The pair zoomed towards Merliah's undersea hometown. She found her mother at the palace, preparing for the forthcoming Changing of the Tides ceremony.

"Every twenty years, a member of the Royal Family must return to the city of Aquellia, sit atop the ancient throne, and regain the power to make Merillia," Calissa explained.

Merliah felt guilty. She knew the ceremony was important - Merillia was the life force of the ocean –but she could not attend the ceremony because it clashed with the surf competition.

49

Merliah felt bad as she returned to the surface. Her mother had been hurt by her refusal to attend the ceremony, but she had worked so hard to qualify for the Invitationals, she couldn't miss out!

Two days later Merliah was in Australia, riding the waves and attempting to beat her rival Kylie Morgan in the first heat of the contest. She pulled off some cool moves but wiped out when she tried to do a handstand on her board, which left her in second place behind Kylie. But, despite not winning a surfwear company asked her to model their range!

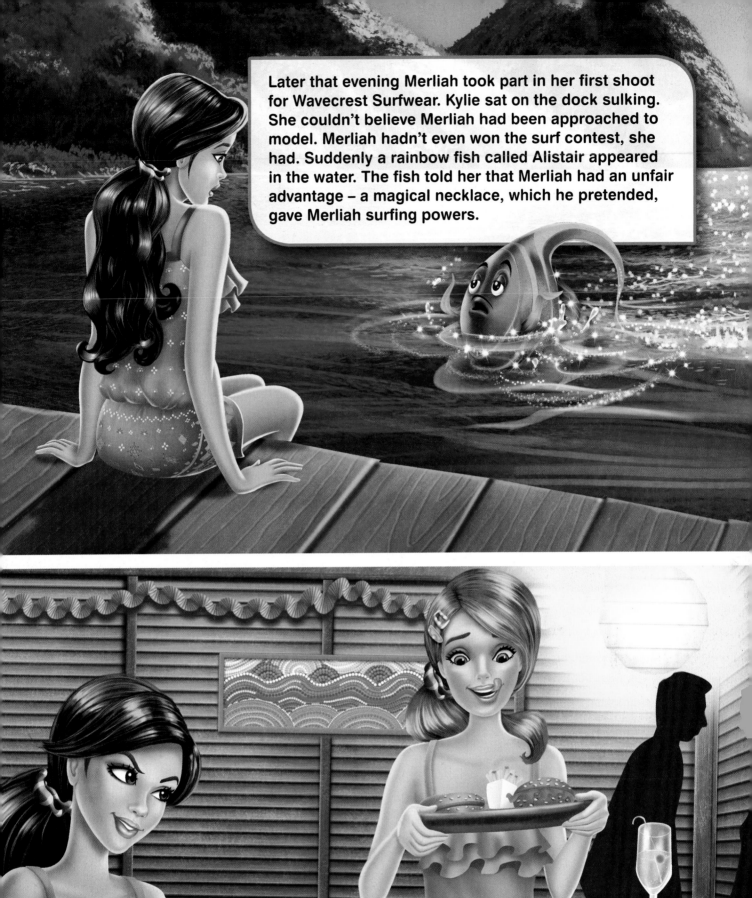

Later that evening Merliah took part in her first shoot for Wavecrest Surfwear. Kylie sat on the dock sulking. She couldn't believe Merliah had been approached to model. Merliah hadn't even won the surf contest, she had. Suddenly a rainbow fish called Alistair appeared in the water. The fish told her that Merliah had an unfair advantage – a magical necklace, which he pretended, gave Merliah surfing powers.

He suggested Kylie take it for herself. Kylie didn't know that the fish was in fact working for Merliah's evil aunt Eris, who'd been banished from Oceana by Calissa. Merliah had taken her necklace off while modelling, so it was easy for Kylie to steal it.

Kylie returned to meet Alistair and, following his instructions put on the necklace and wished to become a mermaid. She couldn't believe it when that wish came true and her legs vanished, replaced by a mermaid's tail.

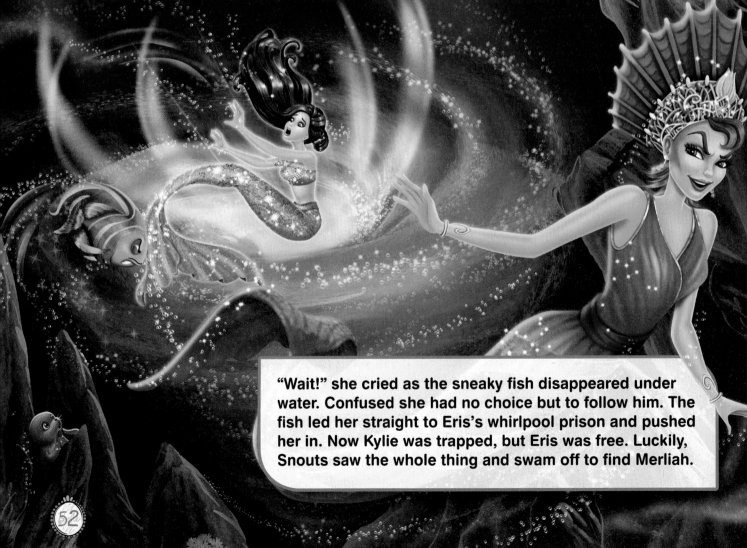

"Wait!" she cried as the sneaky fish disappeared under water. Confused she had no choice but to follow him. The fish led her straight to Eris's whirlpool prison and pushed her in. Now Kylie was trapped, but Eris was free. Luckily, Snouts saw the whole thing and swam off to find Merliah.

"We have to make sure I'm on the throne of Aquellia at mid-day. Then I'll have the power to make Merillia and the ocean will be mine!" Eris cackled. She swam off plotting and, using her magic, managed to force some menacing Stargazer fish into working with her.

Meanwhile Snouts the seal had reached the shore. He told Merliah that Alistair had trapped Kylie and freed Eris.

Realising Kylie must have her necklace; Merliah knew she had to try to save Kylie. Even though without wishing on her necklace, she couldn't fully transform into a mermaid, she could still breathe underwater and she and Snouts headed to the whirlpool, where they used strands of Kelp to haul Kylie out, almost getting trapped themselves in the process.

Down in Oceana, Calissa was unaware of the threat she and her subjects were facing. She welcomed the four Royal Ambassadors. Kattrin, Selena, Mirabella and Renata and together they dry up for the Changing of the Tides ceremony. Each Ambassador placed a precious gem into a special lantern, and then Calissa invited them for a ceremonial tea, while they awaited the mid-day sun. But...

"You're not setting a place for me?" snarled Eris, suddenly emerging from the shadows flanked by the intimidating Stargazers and Alistair.

54

"I don't know how you escaped, Eris, but you will not interfere with the Changing of the Tides Ceremony," said Calissa, squaring up to her evil sister. "You have one chance to end this peacefully. Turn back and leave us. Now."

But a peaceful exit was not on the agenda for Eris. Before Calissa could do anything she and the Ambassadors were surrounded. Eris put evils spells on the Ambassadors, trapping them in a cage and turned Calissa's tail to stone. The Queen of Oceana was helpless; she sank down, down, down into the murky depths of the deep.

To be continued...

MER-MORY game

Grab a watch or ask someone to time you as you look at the picture below for one minute.

When the minute is up, cover the picture with a piece of card or ask someone to cover it with their hand while you try to answer the questions below. Then check page 77 to see how sharp your memory is.

1. How many stripes are there up the centre of Merliah's surfboard?

2. What two colours are her shorts?

3. What is Kylie doing with her arms?

4. What is the lady from the surfwear company wearing?

5. What does she have on the arm nearest you in the picture?

6. How many photographer's cameras can you see clearly in the picture?

7. Which object is one of the crowd holding up?

8. What is the colour of the boy on the left's t-shirt?

Surf's Up

Merliah and Kylie are awesome surfers and look magnificent carving their boards through towering waves and zipping through barrels. A photographer has snapped them mid-competition and a surfing magazine wants to print the picture, but unfortunately it has ripped. Can you put the pieces back together? When you've done this, you'll find the letters make a surf-related word.

1 — W
2 — S
3 — V
4 — E
5 — A

The correct order for the numbers is 1 2 3 4 5
Write the hidden word into Merliah's favourite phrase below.

"Let's ride these WAVES!"

Now why don't you use this page to make a poster of all the things that rock your world? **Use coloured pens and pencils, or make a collage using pictures ripped from magazines.**

Barbie™

BARBIE'S

A B C D

A is for Acting. It's my passion in life.

B is for BFFs. I can't imagine life without my best girlfriends Teresa and Nikki.

C is for Cupcakes. Fun to bake, they're the perfect sweet treat.

D is for Dreamhouse. I'm so lucky live somewhere special.

I J K L M

I is for interviews. I do a lot of these when I'm promoting my latest movie.

J is for Jewellery. It's a great way to add some bling and liven up an outfit

K is for Ken – of course!

L is for Lacey. So cute. So teeny-tiny.

M is for Malibu. My favourite p to hang ou

R S T U V

R is for Ryan and Raquelle. They can be tricky characters, but I love them both.

S is for Sequin. It was love at first sight when I found my gorgeous poodle.

T is for Tennis. Summer's really got me into the sport.

U is for USA – the country where I live.

V is for Vinta Pieces. Tere and I ove add personal touc to our outfit

A-Z

E F G H

E is for Extrovert. I'm quite outgoing and I love to make new friends.

F is for Family. I just love my sisters, sooooo much.

G is for Guitar. I love music, my guitar and piano. I love performing with my friends.

H is for Horse riding. I love to canter Tawny on the beach.

N O P Q

N is for Nail Polish – glittery or metallic colours if possible.

O is for Overtaking. I do this a lot when I'm car racing on the track.

P is for Pink, pink and more pink. Totally my favourite shade

Q is for Quirky – the best way to describe Teresa's amazing style.

W X Y Z

W is for Wardrobe. I heart my walk-in closet. A girl's gotta look her best!

X is for X-rays. I sometimes see these when I'm helping out at the zoo or vets.

Y is for You. I'm glad we're friends!

Z is for Zest for life. My friends tell me I have this and that they love my positive energy.

Barbie

Barbie

Calissa felt hopeless, her stone tail anchored her to the ocean floor. But her loyal friend Zuma the dolphin had followed her as she sank. Zuma couldn't lift Calissa herself so she took off to find Merliah.

Barbie
in
A Mermaid Tale 2
Part Two

Kylie and Merliah were heading for Aquellia. Kylie was pulling Merliah along as she couldn't keep up without her tail and Merliah was telling her how Eris, now she was free, would try to gain the power to make Merillia at the Changing of the Tides Ceremony, so that she could command the sea. Suddenly, they bumped into Zuma who told them what Eris had done to Calissa.

The girls followed the dolphin to the bottom of the ocean where they found Calissa. Merliah apologised to her mother for putting surfing before her royal mermaid duties and Calissa forgave her.

But Merliah and Kylie couldn't rescue Calissa. The girls had no choice but to leave Calissa and head to Aquellia.

While they swam, Merliah made a plan; they would use strands of Kelp to lasso the Stargazers and use them against Eris.

"So it's the four of us against a gang of electric fish with super-sharp teeth: plus your aunt who can point to us and make our worst nightmares come true," sighed Kylie. "Pretty much," laughed Merliah.

The plan was risky, but it worked. Merliah, Kylie, Snouts and Zuma ambushed the Stargazers from below and looped large lassos of kelp over their tails. Jumping on their backs they turned on Eris, who was already sitting upon the throne.

The imprisoned Ambassadors watched helplessly as a battle raged around them. Zuma and Snouts began to inch their cage off a ledge, hoping it would break open and free the Ambassadors. Eris threw out bolts of magic, but Merliah and Kylie dodged them and rode their bucking Stargazers towards her.

Just as Eris was about to turn her magic on Merliah, the first ray of sun cut through the water. It distracted Eris so Kylie used her mighty fish's electric barb to shock Eris off the great seat. Merliah seized her chance and jumped onto the throne but...

64

"NO!" Eris had recovered. She shot a magic bolt at her niece.

It was right on target but before it could hit Merliah, Kylie jumped in the way. The bolt missed her, but hit the Stargazer she was riding throwing Kylie off onto some rocks where she bumped her head.

Eris blasted one of the gems, but Kylie replaced it with a shiny seashell just in time and the light cast a beam on the throne. Merliah could perform the ritual.

"With the changing of the tides, Merillia power will arise.
The royal mermaid on the throne, her fullest mer-self now is known."
Nothing happened.

"No transformation... No Merillia," cackled Eris, closing in on a shocked Merliah. "I'm the only Royal Family member who can do it, so get out of my way!"

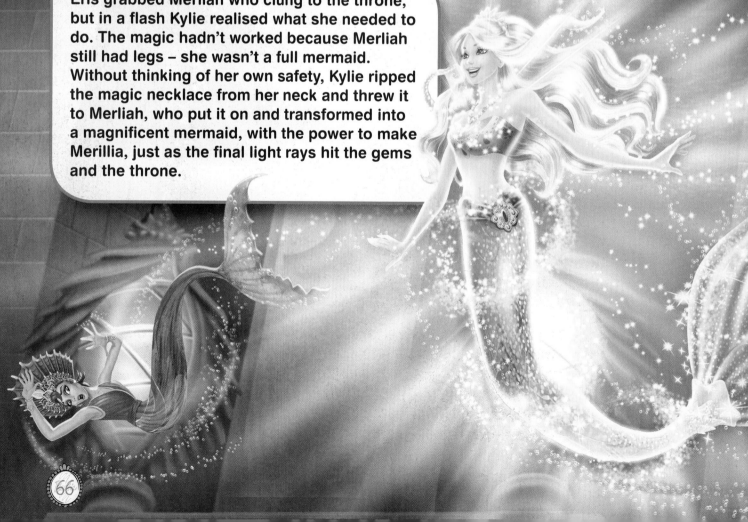

Eris grabbed Merliah who clung to the throne, but in a flash Kylie realised what she needed to do. The magic hadn't worked because Merliah still had legs – she wasn't a full mermaid. Without thinking of her own safety, Kylie ripped the magic necklace from her neck and threw it to Merliah, who put it on and transformed into a magnificent mermaid, with the power to make Merillia, just as the final light rays hit the gems and the throne.

"Nooooooooooooooo!" screamed Eris, seeing her plan had failed. She threw out one last, desperate bolt of magic, but it was too late. The magic from the throne itself repelled her spell and Eris was thrown into a bed of kelp, her powers gone.

The Ambassadors' cage vanished and they instantly regained their strength, speed and beauty, but Merliah could not yet celebrate. Her friend Kylie, now in human form, was drowning. She took her in her arms, slipped the necklace over her and willed her to speak the mermaid wish. The words were faint, but as Kylie whispered them she transformed back into a mermaid and breathed again.

"You saved us all!" cried Calissa, who had been able to swim back home once Eris had lost her powers. "I'm so proud of you. Both of you."

Calissa, Merliah and Kylie looked at Eris whose tail had been replaced by legs. She was now trapped in her own worst nightmare. Leaving the evil ex-mermaid in the hands of the Ambassadors and with the ocean safe once more, they swam back to the surface.

The finals of the Australian Invitational were about to start. Kylie took the necklace off, wished to be human and her legs reappeared. Calissa told her the necklace now belonged to her.

"Go out there and surf, you're doing it for both of us!" Merliah told her friend.

Merliah watched Kylie run onto her sand and take up her surfboard. She was pleased Kylie would now be able to transform and visit Oceana whenever she liked, but felt sad that she, Merliah would never be able to surf again.

"I had a new trick planned for today's run. I wish I could change so I could show it to Kylie," she sighed.

No sooner had she spoken the words, but her tail turned to legs.

"The ritual transformed you into your fullest self - and I can see now that your fullest self is both mermaid and human," laughed Clarissa.

So Kylie and Merliah competed side by side and when Kylie won and Merliah came second they celebrated together. They were champion surfers but more importantly, amazing mermaids who together, had saved the ocean.

STORY QUIZ

What a great story that was. Wasn't Merliah magnificent?
And how brave was Kylie! Now, let's see how much you can remember...

1. Merliah's surname is

a. Winters ☐

b. Morgan ☐

c. Summers ☐

2. To transform from human to mermaid or back she has to

a. Put on a magic necklace and wish to be human or mermaid ☐

b. Go and see her mother, Calissa ☐

c. Rub a shiny seashell ☐

3. How does Kylie feel when Merliah is asked to model surfwear instead of her?

a. Sad ☐

b. Jealous ☐

c. Worried ☐

4. Who helps Kylie transform into a mermaid?

a. Snouts the seal ☐

b. Alistair the rainbow fish ☐

c. Zuma the dolphin ☐

What does Alistair do to Kylie?

a. He pushes her into Eris' whirlpool prison to take Eris' place ☐

b. He changes her tail to stone so she sinks ☐

c. He puts her under the guard of some menacing Stargazer fish ☐

Why is the Changing of the Tides ceremony important?

a. It gives the power to spin Merillia, the ocean's life force ☐

b. It gives the mer-folk the chance to visit Aquellia ☐

c. It's the only time Merliah comes home ☐

Why does Merliah refuse to go

a. She wants to hang out with Kylie ☐

b. Because it clashes with the Australian surfing competition ☐

c. Because she doesn't get on with the visiting Royal Ambassadors ☐

What does Merliah's clever plot to beat Eris involve?

a. Rescuing Calissa from the bottom of the ocean ☐

b. Asking the Ambassadors to put a spell on Eris ☐

c. Ambushing the Stargazer fish, and turning them on Eris ☐

How does Kylie save the day

a. She sits on the throne and recites the mermaid ritual ☐

b. She gives the necklace to Merliah even though it means she might drown ☐

c. She frees the Ambassadors from their cage ☐

What lesson does Calissa learn in the story?

a. That her daughter's true self is both a human and a mermaid ☐

b. That she should be nicer to her sister Eris ☐

c. Not to allow Merliah to surf ☐

When you've finished turn to the answers on page 77 to see how you did...

Check out this wonderful under-sea poster showing Calissa, Merliah and Kylie and the mer-folk celebrating the fall of Eris. Bring this scene to life with your most vibrant aquatic shades?

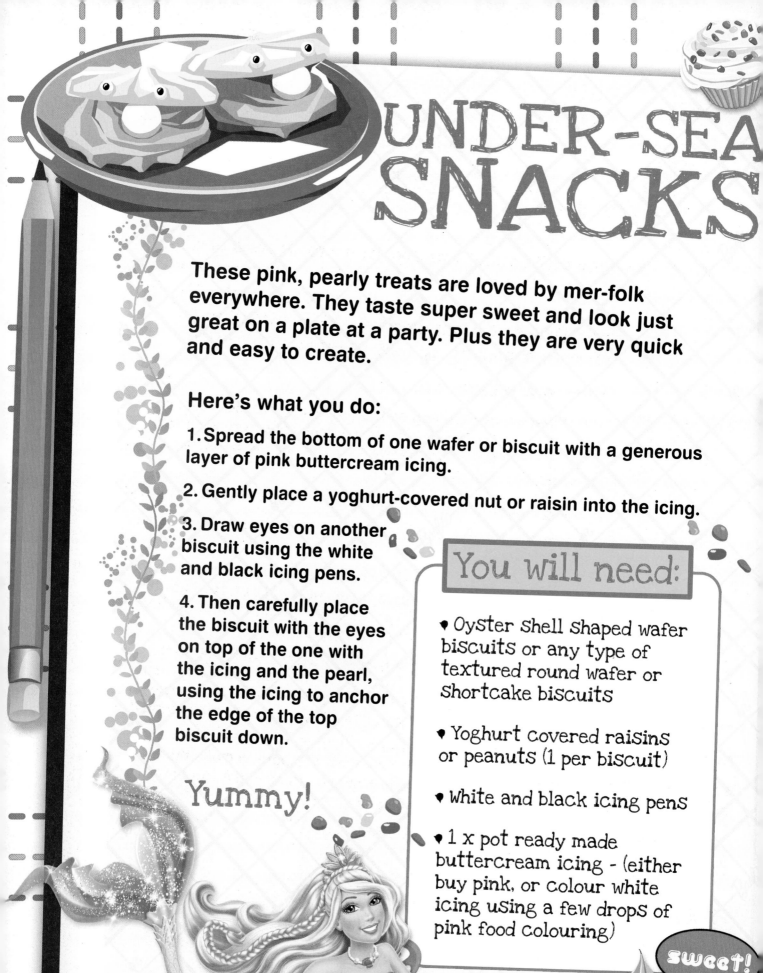

UNDER-SEA SNACKS

These pink, pearly treats are loved by mer-folk everywhere. They taste super sweet and look just great on a plate at a party. Plus they are very quick and easy to create.

Here's what you do:

1. Spread the bottom of one wafer or biscuit with a generous layer of pink buttercream icing.

2. Gently place a yoghurt-covered nut or raisin into the icing.

3. Draw eyes on another biscuit using the white and black icing pens.

4. Then carefully place the biscuit with the eyes on top of the one with the icing and the pearl, using the icing to anchor the edge of the top biscuit down.

Yummy!

You will need:

• Oyster shell shaped wafer biscuits or any type of textured round wafer or shortcake biscuits

• Yoghurt covered raisins or peanuts (1 per biscuit)

• White and black icing pens

• 1 x pot ready made buttercream icing - (either buy pink, or colour white icing using a few drops of pink food colouring)

sweet!

MAKE A MERMAID

Wouldn't you love to dive down to Oceana and meet the mer-folk? Well here's your chance to make your very own mermaid. Perhaps you could make Merliah and Kylie or Calissa and have fun reenacting their story or dreaming up new adventures for them.

Here's what you do:

1. Holding the clothes peg so the notches are at the sides, paint the bottom half of the clothes peg to make the mermaid's tail. The top of the fin, at the mermaid's waist, should be painted in a v shape.

2. Using a contrasting colour paint, give the mermaid a bikini top.

3. Now draw on her eyes and smiley mouth with felt pens

4. Ask an adult to draw a fin shape onto the craft foam and cut it out, then use it as a template to make another fin of exactly the same shape.

5. Squeeze a small blob of glue into the notch of the clothes peg. Stick the 2 fins together with glue and slide them inside the notch to attach the fin to the mermaid.

6. Take a bunch of embroidery floss and trim it to 13cm in length to make the hair. Fold in half and attach to the top of the clothes peg using a dollop of glue.

7. Leave to dry.

You will need:

- Straight wooden clothes pegs - one for each mermaid
- Acrylic paint in bright aquatic shades
- Fine-tipped paintbrushes
- Black and red felt tip pens
- Squares of craft foam in aquatic colours
- Embroidery silk for the hair in blonde and/or red and/or brown and/or black
- PVA or other strong glue
- Scissors

Done!

Bye
from Barbie

Thanks so much for dropping by. I hope you've enjoyed all the stories and activities in my amazing winter annual. I've got so much planned for the year ahead and my new year's resolution is to spend more time with my family. You can write yours in the space at the bottom of the page.

I'd love to hang out with you more, but I'm late for a new year's party so we'll catch up soon.

Happy New Year and lots of love
Barbie
xxx

My new year's resolution is to...

....

....

....

....

Answers

Page 28
POP-TASTIC WORDSEARCH

4. A white skirt, a green top and a black jacket
5. A yellow handbag
6. Two clearly (a third is partially obscured by the flash)
7. A red flag
8. Blue

Page 29
STORY SPOT THE DIFFERENCE

Page 56
Mer-Mory Game

1. Two
2. Pink and blue
3. She has them folded in front of her

Page 57
Surf's Up

1, 5, 3,4, 2 & The hidden word is waves

Page 70
Story Quiz

1. c, 2. a, 3. b, 4. b, 5. a, 6. a, 7. b, 8. c, 9. b, 10. a